THE MAGIC CHANT

A PANDIT AND HIS PUPIL WERE ONCE PASSING THROUGH A FOREST.

SUDDENLY —

HALT! WHO GOES THERE?

ROBBERS!

WE HAVE NO MONEY. PLEASE LET US GO.

HA! HA! YOU CANNOT DECEIVE US WITH HUMBLE TALK AND SIMPLE CLOTHES! IF YOU ARE CARRYING NO MONEY, YOUR PUPIL CAN BRING IT FROM YOUR HOUSE.

THEY BOUND THE PANDIT TO A TREE.

RUN FAST AND BRING A THOUSAND GOLD COINS. ONLY THEN WILL YOUR GURU BE FREED!

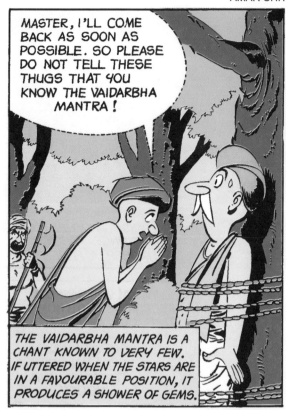

MASTER, I'LL COME BACK AS SOON AS POSSIBLE. SO PLEASE DO NOT TELL THESE THUGS THAT YOU KNOW THE VAIDARBHA MANTRA!

THE VAIDARBHA MANTRA IS A CHANT KNOWN TO VERY FEW. IF UTTERED WHEN THE STARS ARE IN A FAVOURABLE POSITION, IT PRODUCES A SHOWER OF GEMS.

NOW HURRY UP, BOY, AND DO WHAT YOU'VE BEEN TOLD!

I'LL COME BACK WITH THE MONEY IN TWO DAYS.

THAT NIGHT —

HOW COLD IT IS! ALL MY JOINTS ACHE! I WISH I COULD WARM MYSELF NEAR THAT FIRE. BUT THEY WILL KEEP ME TIED TO THIS TREE TILL MY PUPIL RETURNS!

THE PANDIT LOOKED UP AT THE SKY —

OH! THE PLANETS ARE MOVING INTO THE CORRECT POSITION. SHOULD I TELL THE ROBBERS ABOUT THE VAIDARBHA MANTRA AND SO BE FREE AGAIN?

I CAN'T DO IT WITHOUT HAVING A RITUAL BATH AND CHANGING INTO CLEAN SILK CLOTHES...

...AND, OF COURSE, YOU WILL FIRST HAVE TO SET ME FREE!

ALL RIGHT. BUT DON'T PLAY ANY TRICKS OR IT WILL BE THE WORSE FOR YOU!

SO THE PANDIT WAS SET FREE, AND AFTER A DIP IN THE RIVER, HE SAT FOR A LONG TIME, RECITING THE CHANT.

CAN HE REALLY DO IT, OR IS HE FOOLING US?

WILL IT HAPPEN?

HOW LONG WILL IT TAKE?

FINALLY, HE FINISHED.

THE VERY NEXT MOMENT —

GEMS! THOSE ARE PRECIOUS GEMS FALLING DOWN!

QUICK! COLLECT THEM ALL! EVEN THE TINIEST!

GOOD WORK! YOU ARE FREE TO GO NOW.

IT IS A GOOD THING I DIDN'T LISTEN TO MY PUPIL.

BUT, THE NEXT MOMENT —

STAY WHERE YOU ARE! YOU ARE SURROUNDED!

TIE THEM ALL UP!

WAIT! FIRST TELL ME WHY YOU ARE DOING THIS!

WHAT A STUPID QUESTION! FOR YOUR GEMS, OF COURSE.

IS THAT ALL? THEN YOU NEED ONLY TO TAKE CHARGE OF THIS PANDIT HERE.

ANY MORE JOKES FROM YOU, AND YOU'LL BE HUNG UP FROM THE NEAREST TREE!

7

I'LL HIDE BEHIND THIS ROCK AND SURPRISE HIM WHEN HE COMES BACK.

MEANWHILE, THE OTHER ROBBER WENT TO THE VILLAGE NEAR BY AND BOUGHT SOME FOOD. ON HIS WAY BACK —

I'M STARVING. I'LL EAT FIRST AND THEN TAKE THE REST FOR MY FRIEND.

BUT, REALLY, HE IS NO FRIEND OF MINE AT ALL. WHY SHOULD I SHARE ANYTHING WITH HIM?

I WILL SHARE NEITHER FOOD NOR JEWELS WITH HIM. I'LL GET RID OF HIM!

SO HE SPRINKLED SOME POISON ON THE REMAINING FOOD.

THEN HE SET OFF AGAIN.

THIS WILL TAKE CARE OF HIM!

BUT WHEN HE ARRIVED —

THE TREASURE IS ALL MINE NOW!

AAH!

AND NOW, FOR SOME FOOD. AH! I AM AS RICH AS A KING TODAY!

BUT IT WAS ALL IN VAIN. FOR, HAVING EATEN THE POISONED FOOD, HE, TOO, FELL DEAD.

WHEN, TWO DAYS LATER, THE PUPIL RETURNED WITH THE MONEY, HE FOUND THE PLACE LITTERED WITH CORPSES.

MY GURU USED THE CHANT FOR THE BENEFIT OF UNDESERVING PEOPLE! IF ONLY HE HAD HEEDED MY ADVICE!

THE DRUMMER

A DRUMMER AND HIS SON ONCE WENT TO VARANASI TO PLAY AT A FESTIVAL.

AT THE END OF THE FESTIVAL —

AND HERE ARE SOME JEWELS.

AND SOME CLOTHES.

HERE IS SOME MONEY FOR BOTH OF YOU. YOUR SON IS A VERY GOOD DRUMMER.

FATHER, I ENJOYED THE FESTIVAL VERY MUCH.

YOU GAVE A GOOD PERFORMANCE, SON.

THE NEXT MOMENT —

WHAT ARE YOU DOING?

BEATING THE DRUM — WHAT ELSE? I FEEL ON TOP OF THE WORLD TODAY, FATHER!

THE THIEVES QUICKLY SPOTTED THE DRUMMER AND HIS SON.

OH, YES! THOSE TWO CERTAINLY HAVE SOME MONEY IN THOSE HEAVY BUNDLES!

STOP! DON'T MOVE!

GIVE US ALL YOU HAVE!

WHAT A LOVELY NECKLACE!

THE CLOTHES ARE NEW, TOO.

AND THE THIEVES RAN OFF WITH THE LOOT.

I TOLD YOU TO STOP, DIDN'T I? BUT YOU WOULDN'T LISTEN. IN YOUR PRIDE, YOU FOOLISHLY INVITED YOUR OWN DOOM BY PLAYING AT THE WRONG TIME!

I HAVE LEARNT MY LESSON NOW, FATHER!

THE SADHU AND THE RAM

ONE DAY, THERE WAS GREAT EXCITEMENT IN VARANASI. PEOPLE HAD GATHERED TO WATCH A RAM-FIGHT.

A SADHU HAPPENED TO PASS BY.

WHAT IS GOING ON?

A RAM-FIGHT! OH, WHAT FINE BEASTS THEY ARE!

THE SADHU PUSHED HIS WAY IN.

HE SAW A RAM RETREATING WITH HIS HEAD BOWED LOW.

HE IS STEPPING BACK! HE IS BOWING BEFORE ME!

O, NOBLE BEAST! ONLY YOU, IN THIS WHOLE CROWD OF PEOPLE, KNOW A GREAT SOUL WHEN YOU SEE ONE!

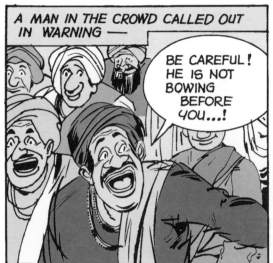

A MAN IN THE CROWD CALLED OUT IN WARNING —

BE CAREFUL! HE IS NOT BOWING BEFORE YOU...!

...HE IS PREPARING TO ATTACK! PLEASE STEP BACK!

NO, I WON'T! THE POOR ANIMAL WANTS ME TO BLESS HIM!

A MOMENT LATER —

A-A-H!

I HAVE INVITED THIS AGONY ON MYSELF! I WAS FOOLISH AND VAIN! NOW I HAVE PAID THE PRICE!

THE DAY THE EARTH BROKE INTO TWO

ONE DAY A RABBIT WAS RELAXING UNDER A BILVA TREE ...

...WHEN A STRANGE THOUGHT STRUCK HIM —

I WONDER WHAT WILL HAPPEN IF THE EARTH BREAKS INTO TWO?

JUST THEN, A BILVA FRUIT FELL FROM THE TREE...

THUD

WH... WHAT IS THAT?

...AND ROLLED OVER DRY PALM LEAVES.

IS THE EARTH REALLY GOING TO BREAK? I MUST RUN AWAY TO A SAFE PLACE!

VERY SOON A PANIC-STRICKEN TROUPE WAS FLEEING THROUGH THE FOREST.

THEN A LION CAME BY ———

WHAT'S GOING ON HERE?

OH, DON'T YOU KNOW? THE EARTH IS BREAKING!

HMM.... BUT THAT IS IMPOSSIBLE!

HE CLIMBED TO THE TOP OF A HILL AND ROARED.

GR-GR-GR-GR

THE ANIMALS FROZE IN THEIR TRACKS.

WHY ARE YOU RUNNING? WHAT IS THE MATTER?

THE EARTH IS BREAKING, O MIGHTY ONE!

WE MUST GO AWAY FROM HERE!

WHO SAW THIS HAPPEN?

THE ELEPHANT. ASK HIM!

NO, NO. NOT ME. ASK THE TIGER.

OH, NO! THE PANTHER REPORTED IT TO ME. ASK HIM!

FINALLY, THE RABBIT WAS BROUGHT TO THE LION.

DID YOU REALLY SEE THE EARTH BREAKING, LITTLE ONE?

YES, MY LORD. I SAW IT WITH MY OWN EYES.

TELL ME, WHERE WAS THIS?

IT WAS NEAR MY BURROW WHICH IS UNDER A BILVA TREE IN A PALM GROVE.

WHEN THEY REACHED THE PALM GROVE —

SHOW ME THE PLACE WHERE YOU HEARD THE NOISE. DON'T BE AFRAID. I'M HERE TO PROTECT YOU.

THAT'S THE BILVA TREE WHERE I HEARD THE THUNDERING NOISE!

ALL RIGHT. YOU WAIT FOR ME HERE. I'LL GO AND LOOK AROUND.

THE LION LOOKED CLOSELY AT THE PALM LEAVES UNDERNEATH THE BILVA TREE.

AH! JUST AS I THOUGHT! THE SOUND OF THE FRUIT FALLING ON DRY LEAVES FRIGHTENED THE RABBIT AND HE THOUGHT THAT THE EARTH WAS BREAKING.

RETURNING TO THE WAITING ANIMALS, THE LION TOLD THEM WHAT HE HAD DISCOVERED.

FRIENDS, YOU DID NOT CHECK IF THIS WAS TRUE. BLINDLY RELYING ON A FALSE RUMOUR, YOU WOULD HAVE PAID A HEAVY PRICE TODAY.

THE FOOLISH TREE

LONG AGO, TWO TREES LIVED IN PEACE AND FRIENDSHIP IN A FOREST WHICH WAS FULL OF WILD BEASTS.

LIONS AND TIGERS ROAMED FREELY IN THE FOREST AND PREYED ON OTHER ANIMALS.

AFTER THEY HAD HAD THEIR FILL, THEY LEFT THE CARCASSES BEHIND...

...CAUSING A FOUL STENCH ALL ROUND. THE FOREST WAS REEKING WITH THE SMELL. ONE DAY —

FRIEND, THESE ANIMALS ARE SUCH A NUISANCE! I FEEL SUFFOCATED BY THE SMELL.

YES, IT IS BECOMING DIFFICULT TO LIVE HERE.

24

THE TREE SHOOK ITSELF VIGOROUSLY, MAKING A LOUD NOISE...

SHR-SHR-SHR!

...WHICH AWAKENED THE ANIMALS SLEEPING BENEATH IT.

WHAT'S HAPPENING?

LOOK AT THAT TREE!

HOW IT IS SWAYING!

THE TREE IS POSSESSED!

LET'S RUN AWAY!

YES, ALL OF US HAD BETTER LEAVE!

HURRY!

THE NEXT MORNING —

AT LAST, I'VE GOT RID OF THOSE ANIMALS! ALREADY, THE AIR SMELLS FRESHER!

MANY DAYS PASSED. QUIET AND PEACE REIGNED IN THE FOREST. THEN ONE AFTERNOON, A COWHERD PASSED THAT WAY.

SH...O...O... COME BACK, YOU NAUGHTY ONE! THE LION WILL EAT YOU UP!

FOLLOWING THE CALF, THE BOY VENTURED INTO THE FOREST.

I HOPE A TIGER DOESN'T POUNCE ON ME!

BUT THERE SEEM TO BE NO TIGERS HERE! AND NO ANIMAL FOOTPRINTS ANYWHERE AROUND!

HE WENT HOME AND TOLD HIS FAMILY ABOUT THIS DISCOVERY. THE NEXT DAY —

IT LOOKS AS IF NO ANIMALS HAVE LIVED HERE FOR AGES!

HE IS RIGHT!

THIS LAND COULD BE VERY USEFUL TO US.

THE TREE SHOOK ITSELF VIOLENTLY, MAKING A LOUD SOUND —

THE TREE TRIED AGAIN.

OH! IT'S NOTHING TO WORRY ABOUT! JUST A FEW TWIGS HAVE FALLEN DOWN! WE'LL CUT DOWN THESE TREES. THE WOOD WILL COME IN USEFUL.

SOON THE FOREST WAS FULL OF PEOPLE FROM THE VILLAGE NEAR BY.

JUST A FEW MORE STROKES, BROTHER!

YES, THEN THE TREE WILL FALL DOWN.

WE'LL TACKLE THIS TREE TOMORROW.

THEY'RE POINTING TO ME! WHAT SHALL I DO?

THAT NIGHT —

HELP, FRIEND! HELP ME, PLEASE! YOU HEARD THEM, DIDN'T YOU? THEY ARE COMING FOR ME TOMORROW!

IT IS TOO LATE! NOW YOU MUST BEAR THE CONSEQUENCES OF YOUR ACTION!

AND THAT WAS THE END OF THE TREE.

THE LOST GRAM

ONCE A KING AND HIS ARMY HAD ENCAMPED OUTSIDE A CITY.

A MONKEY WATCHED THEM CLOSELY FROM A TREE.

I HAVE BEEN FEELING HUNGRY ALL DAY BUT NOW IT APPEARS I'LL HAVE A FEAST!

A LITTLE LATER —

LET'S ROAST SOME GRAM FOR THE HORSES.

HA! JUST AS I EXPECTED. HOW LUCKY I AM!

WE'LL FEED THE HORSES WHEN THE GRAM GETS COLD.

THIS IS MY CHANCE!

AS THE SOLDIERS TURNED TO LEAVE, THE MONKEY SWOOPED DOWN FROM THE TREE...

... AND ATE A HANDFUL OF GRAM.

THIS IS DELICIOUS!

BUT THOUGH HIS HUNGER WAS SATISFIED, HIS GREED WAS NOT.

I MUST TAKE AWAY AS MUCH AS I CAN!

HE STUFFED HIS MOUTH WITH GRAM...

... AND GRABBED SOME MORE WITH BOTH FRONT PAWS.

I'LL HAVE ENOUGH FOR MANY MORE DAYS!

HA! NOW I'LL EAT SOME MORE!

BUT ONE GRAIN ROLLED OUT AND...

...FELL ON THE GROUND.

OH... OH, MY GRAM! IT'S GONE!

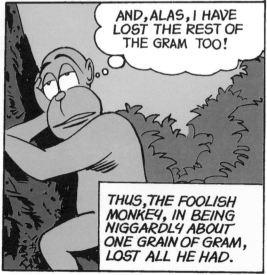

THE GIANT AND THE DWARF

A JATAKA TALE OF WIT AND WISDOM

The route to your roots

THE GIANT AND
THE DWARF

They make an odd couple. Bhimasena is a giant who weaves delicate baskets for a living. His friend the dwarf, who is a wizard with a bow and arrow, is known as the Little Bowman. Together, their antics take us on a roller-coaster ride of humour and adventure, from their rustic village homes all the way to the king's inner circle. In true Jataka tradition, their tale also teaches us a valuable lesson or two.

Script	Illustrations	Editor
Luis Fernandes	Souren Roy	Anant Pai

Cover illustration by: C.M. Vitankar

THE GIANT AND THE DWARF

IN ANCIENT INDIA THERE ONCE LIVED A DWARF.

COMICAL THOUGH HE LOOKED, HE WAS EXCEEDINGLY CLEVER. AND HE HAD ONE GREAT TALENT.

TWANG!

ZZAT!

THUD

HE WAS AN EXCELLENT ARCHER AND PEOPLE CALLED HIM LITTLE BOWMAN.

HEY, LOOK AT THAT LITTLE FELLOW!

HE LOOKS SO FUNNY.

1

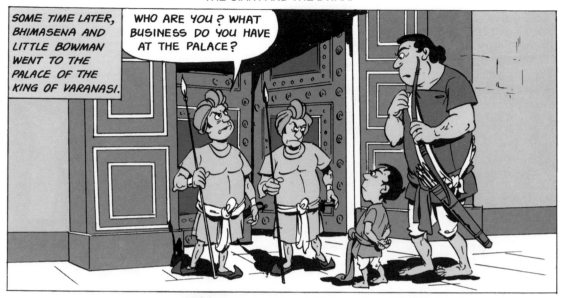

SOME TIME LATER, BHIMASENA AND LITTLE BOWMAN WENT TO THE PALACE OF THE KING OF VARANASI.

WHO ARE YOU? WHAT BUSINESS DO YOU HAVE AT THE PALACE?

I...I AM BHIMASENA, A MIGHTY WEAV...I MEAN, ARCHER. I HAVE COME TO OFFER MY SERVICES TO THE KING.

STOP TREMBLING!

IS HE WITH YOU?

YES! YES!

YOU MAY GO IN.

THE KING WAS IMPRESSED BY BHIMASENA'S SIZE.

SO YOU WANT TO ENTER MY SERVICES AS AN ARCHER.

YES, YOUR MAJESTY.

SOON, BHIMASENA SET OUT FOR THE VILLAGE WHERE THE TIGER HAD LAST BEEN SEEN.

WHEN HE GOT THERE —

FRIENDS, I AM A HUNTER. THE KING HAS SENT ME TO RID YOU OF THE TIGER.

BUT I NEED MEN TO FLUSH HIM OUT OF HIS LAIR. ONCE HE IS OUT IN THE OPEN, I'LL DO THE REST.

YOU CAN TAKE ALL THE ABLE-BODIED MEN OF THIS VILLAGE WITH YOU, MY LORD. WE WILL SEND WORD TO THE OTHER VILLAGES, TOO.

WHEN BHIMASENA FINALLY ENTERED THE FOREST, HE HAD SEVERAL HUNDRED VOLUNTEERS WITH HIM.

THE VILLAGERS SET UPON THE TIGER...

...AND BEAT HIM TO DEATH.

THEY'VE KILLED HIM. GOOD! NOW FOR THE SECOND PART OF THE PLAN.

PULLING OUT A CREEPER...

...HE RUSHED BACK TO THE VILLAGERS.

WHERE IS HE? WHERE IS HE?

?

11

BHIMASENA!

OH! OH!

GO AND SLAY THAT BEAST! IT SHOULD BE CHILD'S PLAY FOR YOU.

YES, YOUR MAJESTY.

A WILD BUFFALO CAN BE MORE DANGEROUS THAN A TIGER. I HOPE THE LITTLE BOWMAN DOESN'T LOSE HIS NERVE.

BUT WHEN HE TOLD THE DWARF OF HIS ASSIGNMENT—

IT SHOULDN'T BE A DIFFICULT TASK FOR YOU, BHIMASENA.

FOR ME! WHAT ARE YOU TRYING TO SAY? IF YOU THINK I AM GOING TO WRESTLE WITH WILD BUFFALOES YOU ARE MISTAKEN.

I'M NOT GOING TO ENDANGER MY LIFE BY DOING YOUR WORK FOR YOU! WE AGREED THAT YOU WOULD DO ALL THE WORK, DIDN'T WE?

NOBODY IS ASKING YOU TO ENDANGER YOUR LIFE, BHIMASENA.

DID YOU ENDANGER YOUR LIFE WHEN YOU WENT TO KILL THE TIGER?

AH! THE CREEPER TRICK! NOW WHY DIDN'T I THINK OF IT MYSELF?

WHEN BHIMASENA CAME BACK TO THE PALACE A FEW DAYS LATER, HE HAD THE DEAD BUFFALO WITH HIM.

SO YOU GOT HIM. DID YOU HAVE ANY TROUBLE?

BHIMASENA!

NOW WHAT'S THE MATTER WITH HIM?

OUR HERO IS BACK.

LOOK AT THE SIZE OF THAT BUFFALO!

WELCOME HOME, BHIMASENA! I AM INDEED FORTUNATE TO HAVE YOU IN MY SERVICE.

YOU SHALL BE WELL REWARDED FOR YOUR EFFORTS.

BHIMASENA BECAME EVEN MORE POPULAR. SEVERAL FEASTS WERE GIVEN IN HIS HONOUR.

TELL US HOW YOU KILLED THE BUFFALO, BHIMASENA.

OH, IT WAS NOTHING REALLY.

HE DID PUT UP A TERRIFIC FIGHT. THE EARTH SHOOK UNDER US AS WE STRUGGLED.

LITTLE BOWMAN, THEREAFTER, KEPT OUT OF BHIMASENA'S WAY. BUT THE GIANT HARDLY MISSED HIM. HE NOW HAD SEVERAL FRIENDS, BOTH IN THE COURT...

...AND OUT OF IT. HE SPENT HIS DAYS IN EASE AND COMFORT.

THEN ONE DAY —

YOUR MAJESTY, WE ARE BEING ATTACKED!

THE KING OF THE NORTHERN KINGDOM IS ON HIS WAY HERE WITH A LARGE ARMY.

YOUR MAJESTY, A MESSAGE FROM THE ENEMY.

"SEND OUT YOUR CHAMPION TO FIGHT WITH OUR OWN OR SURRENDER."

WE SHALL FIGHT! WE SHALL UNLEASH THE MIGHTY BHIMASENA ON THEM!

AS BHIMASENA SWAGGERED OUT OF THE PALACE AND WALKED MAJESTICALLY TOWARDS THE WAR ELEPHANT WHICH WAS WAITING FOR HIM —

BHIMASENA!

BHIMASENA, YOU'LL NEED SOMEONE TO CARRY YOUR SPEAR, WON'T YOU? I'LL COME WITH YOU.

GO, BHIMASENA. CRUSH THEIR CHAMPION AND WIN LAURELS FOR YOURSELF AND OUR KINGDOM.

VICTORY TO BHIMASENA.

23

FAREWELL.

NOW TO COMPLETE THE TASK WHICH MY WORTHY FRIEND SET OUT TO DO.

IN THE ENEMY CAMP—

WHAT IS THAT LITTLE MAN UP TO?

?

IS HE THEIR CHAMPION?

WE SHALL SOON KNOW WHO HE IS.

LET HIM COME CLOSER. THEN I'LL ...

ARRGH!

AS THE SOLDIERS AND THE ELEPHANTS RUSHED ABOUT IN A STATE OF PANIC, LITTLE BOWMAN CHARGED INTO THEIR MIDST...

...PULLED THE ENEMY KING OFF HIS ELEPHANT...

...AND SPED AWAY WITH HIS PRISONER.

SAVE ME! SAVE ME!

LATER —

YOU HAVE PERFORMED AN AMAZING FEAT, LITTLE BOWMAN. SINGLE-HANDED YOU HAVE CAPTURED THE ENEMY AND PUT HIS ARMY TO FLIGHT.

FROM NOW ON, YOU SHALL HAVE AN HONOURED POSITION IN MY COURT — BETTER EVEN THAN THAT WHICH WAS HELD BY THAT COWARDLY BHIMASENA.

LITTLE BOWMAN BECAME A GREAT HERO AND HIS FAME SPREAD FAR AND WIDE. AS FOR BHIMASENA, HE WAS NEVER HEARD OF AGAIN.

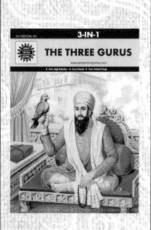

THE PRICELESS GEM

A JATAKA TALE

The route to your roots

THE PRICELESS GEM

Is a glowing stone more valuable than wisdom? Is truth more precious than wealth? Answers to such questions came easily to Aushadha Kumar, a Bodhisattva at the court of King Vaideha. A previous incarnation of the wise and compassionate Gautama Buddha, the tale of his life amidst adversity and courtly rivalry defines the Buddhist ideal of right thinking and right living. This priceless gem from the Jataka fables teaches even as it entertains.

<table>
<tr><td>**Script**
Yagya Sharma</td><td>**Illustrations**
Ram Waeerkar</td><td>**Editor**
Anant Pai</td></tr>
</table>

Cover illustration by: Ram Waeerkar

This tale is based on Maha Ummagga Jataka.

The Priceless Gem

AUSHADHA KUMAR WAS A REINCARNATION OF THE BODHISATTVA.

HE WAS NAMED AUSHADHA* KUMAR, BECAUSE HE WAS BORN HOLDING A DIVINE HERB WHICH HAD SUPER-NATURAL HEALING POWERS.

A YEAR BEFORE AUSHADHA KUMAR'S BIRTH, KING VAIDEHA OF MITHILA HAD A DREAM SIGNIFYING THE ADVENT OF A GREAT SOUL WHOSE WISDOM WOULD BE UNSURPASSED.

EIGHT YEARS LATER, CONVINC-ED THAT AUSHADHA WAS THAT GREAT SOUL, KING VAIDEHA ADOPTED HIM AND BROUGHT HIM TO MITHILA.

AT MITHILA, WHILE AUSHADHA GREW UP INTO A HANDSOME YOUNGSTER, THE PANDITS OF THE COURT, WHO NEVER WANT-ED HIM THERE IN THE FIRST PLACE BECAME ENVIOUS OF HIM.

* MEDICINE

SENAKA, A COURT PANDIT AND THE CHIEF COUNSELLOR, OBSERVED THAT VAIDEHA'S HEART WAS SET ON THE GEM.

IF I RETRIEVE IT, THE KING WILL HAVE GREATER FAITH IN ME THAN HE HAS IN AUSHADHA KUMAR.

SO BEFORE VAIDEHA COULD APPROACH AUSHADHA KUMAR —

I SHALL RECOVER THE GEM RIGHT AWAY, MAHARAJ.

ALL RIGHT, SENAKA.

COME ON MEN, DRAIN THE TANK.

WAIT! THAT IS NOT THE...

PLEASE DO NOT INTERFERE. THE TASK HAS BEEN ASSIGNED TO ME.

WHAT! THE GEM HAS VANISHED!

HM...M...MPH! THEN HAVE THE TANK REPAIRED AND REFILLED.

SOON THE TANK WAS FILLED AGAIN WITH WATER AND LO! THERE WAS THE GEM, GLITTERING AWAY AS BEFORE.

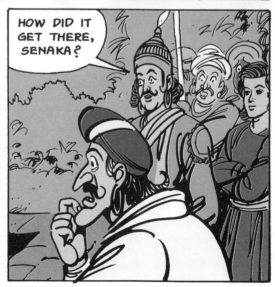

HOW DID IT GET THERE, SENAKA?

THE GEM IS NOT IN THE TANK.

THEN HOW IS IT SEEN THERE?

BRING ME A THALI* AND I WILL SHOW YOU HOW.

A THALI WAS BROUGHT. AUSHADHA FILLED IT WITH WATER AND HELD IT OUT.

MAHARAJ, THE GEM YOU SEE IN THIS THALI...

...IS ONLY A REFLECTION. THE REAL GEM IS IN THE CROW'S NEST IN THAT PALM TREE.

* BRASS PLATE

CAW, CAW.

AUSHADHA KUMAR PRESENTED THE PRICELESS GEM TO THE KING.

WELL DONE, AUSHADHA!

AROUND THIS TIME A YOUNG MAN NAMED PINGUTTAR, WHO HAD COMPLETED HIS STUDIES, WAS TAKING LEAVE OF HIS TEACHER WHEN—

WAIT, SON! TRADITION DEMANDS THAT YOU, MY SENIORMOST DISCIPLE, SHOULD WED MY ELIGIBLE DAUGHTER.

BUT SIR... I... ER...

YOUNG MAN, TRADITION MAKES US WHAT WE ARE.

WE MUST OBEY THE DICTATES OF TRADITION AT ALL COSTS.

SHE IS SO BEAUTIFUL AND I AM SO HOMELY.

AND SHE IS FAR MORE INTELLIGENT THAN I AM.

I SHALL ALWAYS FEEL INFERIOR TO HER. I MUST GET RID OF HER SOMEHOW.

SOON, THEY CAME UPON A GOOLAR* TREE IN THE JUNGLE. PINGUTTAR SUDDENLY FELT HUNGRY.

I WILL EAT SOME GOOLARS.

HE CLIMBED UP THE TREE AND STARTED GOBBLING THE FRUIT.

* WILD FIG.

PLEASE PLUCK SOME FOR ME TOO.

PLUCK THEM YOUR-SELF.

HIS POOR WIFE WAS FORCED TO CLIMB THE TREE.

THE MOMENT SHE CLIMBED UP, PINGUTTAR CAME DOWN...

...QUICKLY COLLECTED AS MANY THORNY TWIGS AS HE COULD...

...AND PLACED THEM AROUND THE TRUNK OF THE TREE.

WHAT ARE YOU DOING?

GETTING RID OF YOU. I DID NOT WANT TO MARRY YOU, YOUR FATHER FORCED YOU ON ME.

I AM OFF. IF YOU TRY TO COME DOWN, THE THORNS WILL PRICK YOU.

HIS HAPLESS WIFE WAS STRANDED IN THE TREE.

A FEW DAYS LATER—

WHAT IS THAT WOMAN DOING UP THERE ON THAT TREE?

I WILL FIND OUT, SIR.

WHEN THE WOMAN NARRATED HER STORY—

HE MUST HAVE BEEN OUT OF HIS MIND TO ABANDON SUCH AN EXCEPTIONAL BEAUTY.

WHAT SHALL WE DO ABOUT HER?

IT IS A KING'S DHARMA TO PROTECT THE UNPROTECTED.

HEEDING THE ADVICE OF HIS MINISTER, KING VAIDEHA BROUGHT HER TO HIS PALACE.

EVEN IN THE HOUR OF CRISIS SHE WAS SO CALM. SHE IS FIT TO BE A QUEEN.

THE WISE SAY THAT A WOMAN ABANDONED BY HER HUSBAND CAN REMARRY. WILL YOU MARRY ME?

GLADLY, O NOBLE KING!

AND ON AN AUSPICIOUS DAY, THE KING MARRIED HER.

YOU ARE NOW BEGINNING A NEW LIFE. SO I MUST GIVE YOU A NEW NAME.

SINCE I FOUND YOU ON AN UDUMBARA* TREE, I SHALL CALL YOU UDUMBARA DEVI.

* WILD FIG - GOOLAR

KING VAIDEHA AND QUEEN UDUMBARA DEVI LED A HAPPY LIFE FOR SOME TIME.

THEN, ONE DAY —

THAT MAN? HE LOOKS LIKE...

YES, IT IS HIM. WHAT A FATE!

AND THE QUEEN SUDDENLY SMILED. THE KING SAW HER SMILE AND BECAME ANGRY.

HOW DARE YOU SMILE AT A STRANGE MAN?

HE IS THE MAN WHO ABANDONED ME.

SO YOU ARE STILL INTERESTED IN HIM.

BELIEVE ME, I AM NOT!

YOU LIE! I SHALL HAVE YOU BE-HEADED!

I AM INNOCENT.

YOUR COUNSELLORS WILL VOUCH FOR THAT.

IF I CONCUR WITH THE KING HE WILL BE PLEASED.

SENAKA! WHAT DO YOU THINK?

MAHARAJ, WOMEN ARE SAID TO BE FICKLE.

AND YOU, AUSHADHA?

MAHARAJ, I BELIEVE WHAT THE QUEEN SAID.

BEING A WOMAN OF NOBLE CHARACTER, SHE COULD NOT HAVE LEFT HER HUSBAND. AND...

...IF HER HUSBAND HAD NOT ABANDONED HER, SHE WOULD BE LEADING A MISERABLE LIFE TODAY.

SO, WHEN I SAW THE PLIGHT OF THE MAN, I COULD NOT HELP BEING PLEASED WITH MY FATE. THAT IS WHY I SMILED.

WHEN THE FACTS WERE VERIFIED, THE KING WAS SATISFIED.

THANK YOU, AUSHADHA. BUT FOR YOU I WOULD HAVE LOST A GEM AMONG WOMEN.

BY THEN, KING VAIDEHA HAD SENSED THAT SENAKA AND OTHER PANDITS WERE ENVIOUS OF AUSHADHA. TO PROVE AUSHADHA'S WISDOM, VAIDEHA POSED A RIDDLE TO THEM.

I WANT TO KNOW WHO IS SUPERIOR, A MAN WHO IS RICH BUT STUPID OR A MAN WHO IS WISE BUT POOR.

THE RICH ONE IS SUPERIOR WITHOUT DOUBT.

WHY?

BECAUSE THE POOR, HOWEVER KNOWLEDGE-ABLE, HAVE TO SERVE THE RICH.

AUSHADHA, WHAT DO YOU HAVE TO SAY?

MAHARAJ, I SAY THE WISE ONE IS FAR SUPERIOR.

WHY?

BECAUSE, THE STUPID SEE WEALTH AS AN END IN ITSELF AND HENCE COMMIT SINS, WHEREAS THE WISE DO NOT AND ARE HENCE VIRTUOUS.

BUT THE RICH HOWEVER STUPID LIVE WELL. THEY MAKE USE OF ALL...

...INCLUDING THE WISE WHO ARE POOR!

NOT FOR LONG. FOR THE RICH WHO ARE STUPID DO NOT HAVE THE SENSE TO EMPLOY WISE ADVISERS.

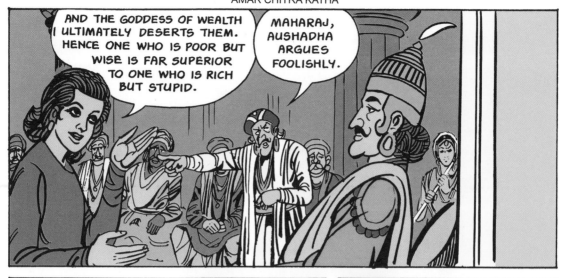

AND THE GODDESS OF WEALTH ULTIMATELY DESERTS THEM. HENCE ONE WHO IS POOR BUT WISE IS FAR SUPERIOR TO ONE WHO IS RICH BUT STUPID.

MAHARAJ, AUSHADHA ARGUES FOOLISHLY.

NOW LOOK AT US. DON'T WE, YOUR COUNSELLORS, THOUGH WE ARE PANDITS, BOW BEFORE YOU? DOES NOT THAT PROVE MY POINT?

ON THE CONTRARY!

KINGS CANNOT FUNCTION WITHOUT WISE COUNSELLORS. HENCE THE WISE ARE DEFINITELY SUPERIOR.

SENAKA COULD NOT REFUTE THAT.

YOUR LOGIC IS ASTOUNDING, AUSHADHA. YOU DESERVE SIXTEEN VILLAGES AS A REWARD.

I AM GRATEFUL, MAHARAJ.

QUEEN UDUMBARA DEVI WAS HAPPY WITH THE GROWING STATUS OF AUSHADHA KUMAR.

YOU SHOULD GET MARRIED NOW. SHALL I FIND A BRIDE FOR YOU?

O QUEEN, I WILL FIND ONE MYSELF.

AND HE MARRIED AMARA DEVI, AN EXTREMELY INTELLIGENT GIRL OF A POOR FAMILY.

MAY YOU BOTH EVER PROSPER. I AM HAPPY FOR YOU.

THEY ARE PLEASED BY HIS CHOICE. NOW HIS STATUS WILL RISE FURTHER, WHILE OURS WILL DECLINE.

DO NOT WORRY. WE WILL HUMBLE AUSHADHA THROUGH HIS WIFE.

AND A FEW DAYS LATER, AFTER THE KING HAD RETIRED TO HIS BEDCHAMBER —

I WILL STEAL THE GEM FROM THE KING'S CROWN AND PLANT IT IN AUSHADHA'S HOUSE.

NOW TO FIX THE ARTIFICIAL GEM IN ITS PLACE.

WHAT A GENIUS I AM!

HEH! HEH! NOW FOR THE NEXT MOVE!

AH, MY BEAUTY! IT HURTS ME TO DROP YOU INTO THIS POT OF CURDS.

THEN SENAKA CALLED HIS MAID.

GO AND HAWK THIS IN THE STREET WHERE AUSHADHA LIVES.

BUT DO NOT SELL IT TO ANYONE EXCEPT AUSHADHA'S WIFE.

I UNDER-STAND, MASTER.

THE MAID SOON REACHED THE STREET WHERE AUSHADHA KUMAR LIVED.

CURDS! SWEET CURDS!

HEY WOMAN! LET ME SEE THOSE CURDS.

THE MAID PAID NO ATTENTION TO THE WOMAN.

HEY! I SAID I WANT TO BUY SOME CURDS.

CURDS! CREAMY CURDS!

DO YOU WANT TO SELL YOUR CURDS OR NOT?

STRANGE! WHY IS SHE HAWKING IF SHE DOES NOT WANT TO SELL?

CURDS! FRESH CURDS!

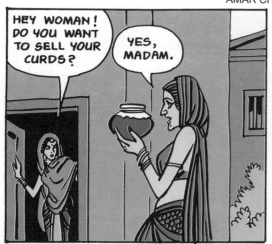

HEY WOMAN! DO YOU WANT TO SELL YOUR CURDS?

YES, MADAM.

HOW MUCH DO YOU WANT?

NOTHING.

BUT YOU MUST ACCEPT SOME MONEY.

NOT FROM YOU, O WIFE OF PANDIT AUSHA-DHA KUMAR.

THE MAID FORCED AMARA DEVI TO ACCEPT THE CURDS FREE.

WHY SHOULD SHE GIVE ME THE CURDS FREE?

QUICK, FOLLOW THAT WOMAN AND TELL ME WHERE SHE GOES.

MEANWHILE IN THE PALACE —

WHERE IS MY CROWN JEWEL? I SHALL HAVE YOU ALL BEHEADED.

MAHARAJ! PARDON ME. BUT...

...IT SEEMS TO BE THE WORK OF AN OUTSIDER.

NO OUTSIDER IS ALLOWED IN THESE QUARTERS.

THEY ARE, MAHARAJ! WHAT ABOUT US AND...

AND!

AND AUSHADHA KUMAR.

WHAT DO YOU MEAN?

ONLY THIS, MAHARAJ, THAT YOU SHOULD HAVE OUR HOUSES SEARCHED.

YOU MUST BE OUT OF YOUR MIND.

I AM NOT, MAHARAJ. I INSIST. BECAUSE WE SHOULD BE ABOVE SUSPICION.

THE HOUSES OF THE FOUR PANDITS WERE SEARCHED, OBVIOUSLY WITH NO RESULTS.

MEANWHILE, THE MAID SENT OUT BY AMARA RETURNED.

THAT WOMAN WENT STRAIGHT TO SENAKA PANDIT'S HOUSE.

BANG! BANG!

OBVIOUSLY SENAKA SENT THIS POT OF CURDS. BUT WHY?

WHO IS IT?

SOLDIERS! OPEN THE DOOR.

A FEW HOURS LATER—

WE FOUND THE JEWEL MAHARAJ, IN AUSHADHA KUMAR'S HOUSE. IT WAS HIDDEN IN A POT OF CURDS.

VERY CLEVER!

VAIDEHA BECAME VERY UPSET. JUST THEN—

MAHARAJ, PANDIT AUSHADHA KUMAR WANTS TO MEET YOU.

I DO NOT WANT TO SEE HIS FACE.

SINCE VAIDEHA WAS NOT EVEN PREPARED TO LISTEN TO HIM, AUSHADHA DECIDED TO LEAVE THE CAPITAL.

I SHALL LIVE INCOGNITO IN A VILLAGE.

HE WENT TO A REMOTE VILLAGE WHERE NOBODY WOULD RECOGNIZE HIM.

GRANDPA, DO YOU NEED AN ASSIS-TANT?

YES, SON, I COULD DO WITH HELP.

AND HE STARTED WORKING AS THE POTTER'S ASSISTANT.

AFTER A FEW DAYS WHEN VAIDEHA HAD CALMED DOWN —

YOU DID NOT GIVE AUSHADHA A CHANCE TO EXPLAIN.

THE JEWEL WAS FOUND IN HIS HOUSE.

BUT THE ACCUSED MUST BE GIVEN A CHANCE TO DEFEND HIMSELF.

YOU ARE RIGHT. I SHALL DO THAT NOW.

A SEARCH PARTY SENT BY THE KING BROUGHT AUSHADHA KUMAR BACK TO THE COURT.

HOW DO YOU EXPLAIN THE RECOVERY OF THE CROWN JEWEL FROM YOUR HOME?

MY WIFE COULD TELL YOU.

WHEN AMARA DEVI WAS SUMMONED TO THE COURT—

MAHARAJ, THE GEM CAME TO OUR HOUSE IN THIS POT.

AND WHO BROUGHT THE POT TO YOUR HOUSE?

A VENDOR OF CURDS. I CAN HAVE HER BROUGHT HERE.

MAIDS! BRING HER IN.

THIS IS THE WOMAN WHO BROUGHT THE POT OF CURDS WITH THE GEM HIDDEN INSIDE.

PARDON ME, MAHARAJ, SENAKA PANDIT GAVE ME THE POT.

YOU, SENAKA?

I...ER...PLEASE PARDON ME, MAHARAJ.

NEVER! YOU SHALL BE SEVERELY PUNISHED.

BEING A BENEVOLENT SOUL, AUSHADHA KUMAR CAME TO SENAKA'S RESCUE.

PARDON HIM, MAHARAJ. IT WAS ONLY A PRANK.

YOU ARE NOBLE, AUSHADHA!

I APPOINT YOU COMMANDER OF MY ARMY.

I AM HONOURED, MAHARAJ.

SENAKA LEFT THE COURT A DEJECTED MAN.

WHATEVER I TRY RECOILS ON ME AND ONLY ADDS TO AUSHADHA'S GLORY.

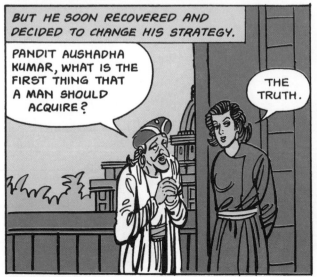

BUT HE SOON RECOVERED AND DECIDED TO CHANGE HIS STRATEGY.

PANDIT AUSHADHA KUMAR, WHAT IS THE FIRST THING THAT A MAN SHOULD ACQUIRE?

THE TRUTH.

AND THEN?

WEALTH.

AND THEN?

MANTRA*

AND THEN?

THE ABILITY TO KEEP A SECRET.

FROM EVERYBODY!

YES! A SECRET SHOULD NOT BE DIVULGED TO ANYONE.

I HAVE GOT YOU AT LAST, AUSHADHA KUMAR!

MAHARAJ, AUSHADHA KUMAR IS UP TO SOMETHING.

SENAKA, STOP WORRYING. YOUR POSITION IS SAFE IN THE COURT.

I AM NOT WORRIED ABOUT MYSELF BUT ABOUT YOU.

ME! WHY?

BECAUSE I THINK AUSHADHA HAS SOME SECRETS WHICH HE WILL DIVULGE TO NO ONE.

I DON'T BELIEVE IT.

* WORDS HAVING MYSTIC POWERS

THE NEXT DAY AT THE COURT—

PANDIT AUSHADHA KUMAR, TO WHOM WOULD YOU CONFIDE YOUR SECRETS?

NO ONE.

NOT EVEN TO THE KING?

YES, NOT EVEN TO THE KING.

AFTER THE COURT WAS ADJOURNED—

THE COMMANDER OF MY ARMY IS SECRETIVE WITH ME! THIS IS AN ALARMING REVELATION INDEED!

DON'T WORRY, MAHARAJ. I WILL TAKE CARE OF THINGS.

MEANWHILE, AS AUSHADHA KUMAR RETURNED HOMEWARDS—

I HAVE NEVER SEEN THE KING LOOK SO PERTURBED.

THIS TIME SENAKA IS UP TO SOMETHING FAR MORE SERIOUS.

AUSHADHA KUMAR KNEW THAT SENAKA AND THE THREE OTHER PANDITS REGULARLY MET IN A SECLUDED CORNER OF THE GRAIN MARKET.

I HAD BETTER FIND OUT WHAT THEY ARE UP TO.

HE HID HIM-
SELF IN A
HEAP OF
GRAIN AND
WAITED.

SOON THE FOUR PANDITS ARRIVED.

I HAVE HATCHED A SECRET PLAN. WE SHALL HAVE AUSHADHA MURDERED.

WILL THE KING APPROVE OF OUR ACT?

HE WILL. BECAUSE I HAVE IMPRESSED UPON HIM THAT AUSHADHA HAS HIS EYES SET ON THE THRONE.

THIS SITUATION CALLS FOR DRASTIC ACTION.

AUSHADHA KUMAR GATHERED THE TROOPS AND SURROUNDED THE PALACE.

SEE THAT NO ONE ESCAPES.

AFTER ESTABLISHING HIS CONTROL OVER THE CITY, AUSHADHA KUMAR WENT TO MEET THE KING.

GLORY TO, KING VAIDEHA!

YOU HYPOCRITE! WHY DO YOU SHOUT MY PRAISES WHEN YOU ARE OUT TO DO ME HARM.

I HAVE NO INTENTION OF HARMING YOU, MAHARAJ. I JUST WANT TO MAKE YOU AWARE OF CERTAIN FACTS.

WHAT FACTS?

SENAKA PANDIT WANTED TO HAVE ME MURDERED.

?!

SO HE POISONED YOUR MIND TO GAIN YOUR SUPPORT.

ARE YOU WONDERING HOW I LEARNT YOUR SECRET, SENAKA?

YOU REVEALED IT TO ME YOURSELF BY SPEAKING OF IT TO OTHERS.

I THINK YOU WILL AGREE NOW THAT A SECRET SHOULD NEVER BE DIVULGED TO ANYONE. FOR...

...THE MOMENT IT IS DIVULGED IT CEASES TO REMAIN A SECRET.

AND, MAHARAJ, I ALSO WANTED TO PROVE THAT I WOULD EVER REMAIN FAITHFUL TO YOU.

EVEN AFTER I WRONGED YOU?

BUT YOU HAVE ALSO BEEN VERY KIND TO ME.

IT IS FORBIDDEN TO BREAK EVEN A BRANCH OF A TREE UNDER WHICH YOU HAVE TAKEN SHELTER...

...BECAUSE THEN IT HAS BECOME YOUR FRIEND. AND...

...IT IS A SIN TO WRONG A FRIEND.

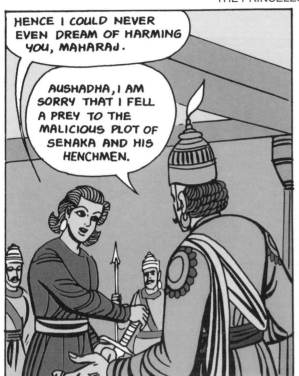

31

SUBSCRIBE NOW!

TINKLE COMBO
MAGAZINE + DIGEST
1 year subscription

Pay only ₹1200
₹880!

FREE
2 Time Compass DVDs worth ₹598

TINKLE
MAGAZINE
1 year subscription

Pay only ₹480
₹380!

I would like a one year subscription for

TINKLE COMBO ☐   **TINKLE MAGAZINE** ☐

(Please tick the appropriate box)

YOUR DETAILS*

Name: .... Date of Birth: |__|__| / |__|__| / |__|__|__|__|

Address: ....

.... City: .... Pin: |__|__|__|__|__|__| State: ....

School: .... Class: ....

Tel: .... Mobile: + 91 - |__|__|__|__|__|__|__|__|__|__|__|

Email: .... Signature: ....

PAYMENT OPTIONS

☐ Cheque /DD:

Please find enclosed Cheque /DD no. |__|__|__|__|__|__| drawn in favour of 'ACK Media Direct Pvt. Ltd.'

at .... (bank) for the amount .... ,

dated |__|__| / |__|__| / |__|__|__|__| and send it to: IBH Books & Magazines Distributers Pvt. Ltd., Arch No. 30,
West Approach, Below Mahalaxmi Bridge, Mahalaxmi (W), Mumbai - 400034.

☐ Pay Cash on Delivery: Pay cash on delivery of the first issue to the postman. (Additional charge of ₹50 applicable)

☐ Pay by money order: Pay by money order in favour of "ACK Media Direct Pvt. Ltd."

☐ Online subscription: Please visit: www.amarchitrakatha.com

For any queries or further information: Email: customerservice@ack-media.com or Call: 022-40497435 / 36